TALES VRUM DEBN

TALES VRUM DEBN

DERRICK V. RUGG

TABB HOUSE
Padstow, Cornwall.

First Published 1985

Tabb House, 11 Church Street, Padstow, Cornwall PL28 8BG.

Printed in Great Britain by Quintrell & Co. Ltd., Wadebridge, Cornwall.

Contents

Permission to reprint stories previously published in *Express and Echo, Pulman's Weekly, Western Morning News,* or by Radio Devon, is gratefully acknowledged, and the provision of drawings by Clare Western.

One-Upmanship

OF COURSE I am well aware that March has its good points. There is the fresh green of new grass called forth by a pale flickering sun, besides the catkins and daffodils.

This year's catkins are splendidly pendulous, and daffodils are gathering in force to march us all towards spring. Daisies show as bold as dandelions, and primroses materialise out of dull clay banks.

Yet there is a concealed snag abroad — something that is liable to hit certain people like the morning after the night before; and I think an exposure is urgently called for. I am referring to a particularly crafty brand of one-upmanship. And I'd better explain.

You go along to a country pub for a quiet half pint. A group of rosy-faced locals are there, and nearly sure to be talking about gardening — or rather, not gardening.

They sit there and agree so beautifully that it is a peculiar pleasure to observe the exercise.

They say that it is no good putting spade to soil: "Would do more harm than good," etc.

"The soil baint warmed up," says Ted.

"I likes to feel the sun on my back," asserts George.

"You can't garden in your overcoat," puts in Jack.

"Shirtsleeves job!" huffs Joe, and so on.

I will ruefully admit that I fell foul of their despicable game, before I got wised up. But take the raw young gardener who has just married and moved into Four Winds or Lark's Rise.

He is hanging on every word, and in order to test that his ears are in good nick, he'll probably move nervously across to one of the pundits and say "So you haven't planted anything yet?"

"Get out wae ee, no! Plenty of time boy! Next month will be soon enough," will be the gist of the response.

The young man is thereby led to believe that there is no rush, and this appears confirmed when he notes that the gardeners have drinking mugs and not gardening forks in their hands.

The fool!

He will find out in due course that sandwiched between the continual con in the local are periods of subtle and feverish activity behind fence and privet hedge. A glance into the gardens of the sons of deception would reveal a great cosseting with straw and polythene; a contrived and precocious 'lew' corner and a tilth sifted grain by grain. You would find boxes of plants ready to go out; all would be shooting and sprouting.

Meanwhile the devious propagators are gloating to themselves, and continuing to preach a misleading gospel that must have landed a multitude of young husbands in the soup.

In due course the lulled unfortunates have the great illusion thrust in their faces.

They see new spuds, spring onions, and lettuce offered to landladies, in a leering, smug, and well-publicised operation.

Broad beans are produced from inside pockets, causing the raw young man to picture his retarded row which is being used for combined ops by the black army.

"The rotters, the blankety blanks!" he mutters. Thereby he has probably learned the lesson.

But there'll be a fresh crop next year.

No that is not quite right.

There will be two crops — early crops and fresh suckers.

Hence I have come to the firm conclusion that it is my duty to pre-empt much horticultural distress by issuing a general warning to the young, the naive, and the trusting among the gardening brotherhood.

Listen not to siren voices of the sun worshippers, the disciples of delay, the propagators of procrastination — who are without doubt scheming away amidst us at this very moment!

Do not be led up the garden path — metaphorically speaking of course. Do not be left up the creek without a paddle — or rather, enticed to hearth and local shrine onionless and radishless, bearing excuses, alongside other rotters who bear gifts.

Start scratching, poking, cosseting and cloche-ing, fellows, right away.

Oh yes, and as a hedge, buy your Ted, George, Bernard — or whoever — a pint once a while. Get me?

Environmental Studies

THERE WERE two roughly parallel conversations going on in The Corn Drill. This was not an unusual occurrence.

One was out in the open, on full volume, and the other quiet, and sort of woven in.

Farmer Spout at the bar: Yes you would be most welcome to bring your pupils to look around my farm.

Young Schoolmaster: I do appreciate that, Mr Spout.

Harry: Watch ver the catch boy!

Sid: Thees be on the bale cart vot tis over, skulemaster.

Farmer Spout: Of course we must harrange a suitable time.

George: Ees, we must harrange that.

Young Schoolmaster: I like the children to get direct experience.

Sid: Be better off in skule learnin summin!

Harry: They kids be gallivantin off somewhere every week.

George: Counting the trees in the orchard across the way tuther afternoon — all taan o' um.

Farmer Spout: Eddification is so much more real, and exciting these days. Difrent vrum my days.

George: Whadder maan?

Sid: Did er ever go to skule? I verget.

Harry: The old man zaand un to zum private skule over Talebare. They couldn't att anything into un by all accounts.

Young Schoolmaster: The idea is to use the environment whenever possible.

George: Sure to be right.

Harry: Whadder maan by 'vironment?

Sid: What's round about ee!

Farmer Spout: The youngsters will need their Wellington boots.

Harry: That they will. Waders wouldn't be put out o' place in thik yard of ees.

Young Schoolmaster: Of course you don't ever do any milking by hand now I take it.

Farmer Spout: No, thank heavens. Hi've had my fill of that as a youngster.

Sid: That's a b...y stretcher.

Harry: Never milked a cow in ees life.

George: Riding about a oss all the time when he waddn't at thik adgicultral college.

Farmer Spout: Things have got very scientific you know. Tidn't so slow - like twas in my Father's days.

Sid: Ees father would jump over ees ead now.

George: Scientific! All they gotta do is look over the aadge and see what tuther feller is up to.

Harry: Fisons tells um ow to farm.

Young Schoolmaster: What sort of milking process do you have?

Farmer Spout: We're on a bulk tank now. It's the latest way.

George: No buckets, no churns. Proper lazy caper.

Sid: Money ver ole rope.

Young Schoolmaster: Of course I would like to follow up by looking at other farm activities.

George: Nort else to see!

Harry: Aytime over in vive minutes — no kale to cut, no mangel to pull.

Sid: Mucking out done wae a gurt shovel fixed on the front of a tractor!

Farmer Spout: Yes, I can show you some hinteresting leys. I specialised in that part of the business at hagricultural college you know. Fortunately Father saw the trend.

Sid: The ole man told me if ee'd listened to ee, ee'd bin bankrupt years ago.

Young Schoolmaster: Good! We can do some soil testing and transects.

George: Better fit they learned um the tables.

Sid: Aaf the youngsters can't add up on the dart board.

Harry: Tuther aaf can't take away.

Young Schoolmaster: Would it be all right to do some fieldwork?

Farmer Spout: Feel free!

George: Generous bain't ee?

Sid: He'll be standing a round in a minute.

Harry: Ang on, I think ees working up to zummin.

Farmer Spout: When you see me on the bale cart one evening

come across and we'll fix things up.
Young Schoolmaster: Fine!
George: Gurt vule!
Sid: Valled right in!
Harry: What did I tull ee?
Exit rare variety: contented farmer, with recruit designate.

Sweet Haying

I WAS in a reminiscing mood in the playground, and before I realised where I was heading I became involved in 'sweet haying' with a female colleague — well, not literally.

"What was sweet haying?" she enquired.

"You know. You must know!" I insisted — or blundered is maybe more accurate.

"I'm not sure that I do," she said. I began a shrugging-off operation.

"Oh, it was just a custom — or more of a lark really — that occurred in hay fields years and years ago. You ought to remember!"

(Eh, that was not so clever!)

Oh well, I was impaled now, and the lady looked hard at me. "Go on!" she coaxed.

"You know what I mean," I said, foolishly trying another ploy. "Haven't you been sweet hayed?" I asked.

"I'm still not with you. Should I have been?" the persistent brunette enquired — or teased. (How could I tell?)

'I would have thought so. I would have thought you would have been sweet hayed.' I said — to myself.

The lady kept looking at me expectantly — tantalisingly perhaps. Where could I shunt next? I took out my handkerchief and snuffled away behind it for a moment as if the resurrected hayfield had brought on hayfever.

I emerged eventually, warily, hopefully.

My lady kept going: "What *are* you on about this time?"

It was no good. I had put my hand to the plough. Or should it be the hay wain?

I rather hoped someone would report a bleeding nose, or inform that two infants were locked in mortal combat behind the hutted classroom. But nobody came, and I was left on the rack with a female and an unfortunate subject.

Is there a worse combination?

I rambled over the hayfields of yesterday; the horses, the wagons, the scent, the refreshing jars. The lot! I awaited results.

"What *was* sweet haying?"

Back to square one!

I looked at the blue hills, the gliding gulls and wisping mares' tails in the sky.

The crunching moment of truth had come.

I went on: "Well, when I was about eight or nine I went on into a hayfield just above the house where I lived in Kentisbeare. I watched as men loaded up Miller Howe's Bedford lorry.

"Then a young willowy blonde entered the field, accompanied by a dusky brunette. I am sure they know the ropes." (Heck, I should not have said that!)

I hurried on: "Ronnie Holmes and Fred Mitchell, who were rolling and pitching hay, transferred to rolling and kissing the girls in the hay stooks. There were ritual screams. They were pretty girls," I added. I was remembering that I wondered what it was all about at the time. Suddenly I realised I was off the hook.

The lady had relaxed visibly. A faraway look came into her eyes.

She fell silent — and I fancied I could smell, in a pungent flash, the fragrance of hay.

I reckoned she'd been rolled — sweet hayed I mean. And yet — well you know ladies as well as I don't.

The Devonshire Disease

AS I walked into the playground of a school in Berkshire, at the beginning of an autumn term some years back, I looked all around, trying to assess at which location on the campus the Head was to be found.

Suddenly a door opened and out rushed a bespectacled, smallish man, who grabbed my hand and pumped vigorously as he declared himself the boss, and then told me what I was going to do.

Why the exuberance? Well, the teacher who was scheduled to take the top class had obtained a new post quite late in the preceding term, and it had appeared that there would be some delay over replacement. Hence the Head, who was clearly not relishing the prospect of having to take the class himself, was very glad when I was sent by the 'Office' to take on the job.

It was a school of around 230 pupils with seven assistant teachers. Five of them were women, and there was just one chap with whom I could discuss football.

The Head was a Devonian, and outside of Devon it is somewhat rare to find a Head of such pedigree. They are frequently Welsh.

Anyway when I got over the shock of finding a chap from North Devon in charge, I settled down and got on quite well — I think.

There was one thing though. The Head had a disease. Well, not really a disease I suppose. It wasn't catching as far as I know. Anyway, I couldn't catch it. I had got it already — though I had not realised it.

The double diagnosis came about this way. One of the ladies was complaining loudly in the staffroom. "That man," she said, "is the limit. I have my bad back, and he says he has it as well, only more so."

"Yes, you will find that about Ron," my young male colleague said. "Wherever you've been or whatever you've done, he can cap it. Only his war wound stopped him playing football for England, and climbing Everest years before Hilary."

"He's had treble pneumonia," joined Mildred from the Infants.

"Naturally he obtained an A+ on teaching practice," added Mrs B. "Though he seems awful shy of using his great talent these days."

"He bowled so fast his opponents used to implore him to drop into a lower gear," went on the young man, "and his darts were so good that some nights the pints he won were lined up four deep on the bar. Pretty good for the great churchwarden!'

"I think it is some trait — some affliction, prevalent where he comes from. He's a North Devon savage, remember!" the lady concluded.

"Hey, I come from Devon," I nearly said. Then I thought the north bit may perhaps have reduced any inference to me as I am an East Devon fellow. But I didn't altogether appreciate the looks I seemed to detect. And I couldn't help thinking...

I had held forth about darts one wet lunchtime, and had bid against the Head on the subject of cricket — until I realised I couldn't win.

The outcome saw me having to admit to myself that I had the capping complaint. Moreover, if you reflect on it, you will see that during my stay at that school I was more than somewhat inhibited. In fact I was really glad when I got back into Wiltshire and could operate among the Moonrakers again.

Then — through some oversight I imagine — I obtained a post in Devon, and circumstances changed again.

I have found that the capping exercise — which is quite incurable by the way — is tricky on my native patch, because you have to deal with an abundance of competitors among the locals, whilst you know that the audience which is so essential to the process is experienced and discriminating. It is apt to be the very devil. You are impelled to operate. But you must be on the top line.

It was difficult the other night in a pub in the Blackdowns. As I walked in, I met several customers going out, one with the hiccoughs. The landlord was standing behind the bar, his eyes glazed and his hands gripping the woodwork.

I sensed the position. An operator was present who was over-playing his hand. This is sad in a way, as it means his pitch is forever lost. But there I was. I ordered a drink and the landlord leapt into life.

"Hello!" said the operator as if he had known me all his life. "I've seen you somewhere before." They nearly always say that. I should know!

I permitted the faintest masquerade of a smile.

The landlord, in contrast, beamed at me, and you could see he regarded himself as let off the hook.

In a moment I was holding a pint, had paid for it, and the landlord — the twister — had disappeared.

I knew the drill. There are only a few seconds before the preliminary probes of conversation. The exponent of the capping art almost always has a drink to clear his throat as he watches what you are going to buy.

It could be just a box of matches and out, for instance, and that pre-empts operations, so to speak.

One ploy by which you can try to avoid being drawn is to put a coin in the juke box and hope it has not been turned down from the night before. But juke boxes drive me mad, and in any case I have a second affliction: I am very tight.

Wait for it! "Petrol! What a price! I remember..."

In a matter of moments your capper was in the Middle East sinking oil wells in the day, and charming all the exotic birds in the spare time.

I couldn't counter there, although my mind was already straining to shift the conversation onto my own ground.

A deft switch to all-in wrestling had occurred before I realised it. If someone would secure one arm behind the operator's back, he would consider tying Giant Haystacks in so many knots that the Chief Scout would funk sorting the job out.

Again no dice. Well, anybody has only to look at me!

The Korean War came next — and then racing pigeons. Foreign country!

Then Alec, the local Council workman, who is inarticulate until he has had four pints, came in. In flashed the landlord, served him and dashed out. "Expecting Uncle Absalom to ring," he said.

Funny that! Tom, a regular, who claimed his beer was flat the

other week, expressed the view, rather crudely I thought, that
there was a certain sparsity of relations. No matter. The operator
was onto birds; owls, eventually.

I think this had something to do with my expression, which
was formed around an open mouth and wide eyes. I must have
resembled a football supporter in a five-nil-down situation.

Wait a minute! "Owls," he was saying.

"Owls!" Then it registered. "Got you!" I said to myself.

I ordered a pint and bought the landlord a half. He thanked
me grimly as he felt obliged to stay.

"I kept this owl," said the operator, "in my study until the
wife began to claim he damaged the Chippendale."

He — the owl that is — was very intelligent too; listened to
the news and brought rats home five at a time all wrapped up in
a polythene bag, ready to store if necessary in the deep-freeze.

My chance was coming up, and as I simulated interest I was
gauging the launching point for my entry.

The operator slurped a drink hurriedly as he proceeded to
take breath and change gear. That is the time to jump in, and I
was away: "I was living in this thatched cottage that my great-
uncle Sir Sebastian had left my grandmother in his will. . .

"One morning I got up all excited because I had been invited
by Lord Firewater the night before, in the lounge of the Peacock
Arms, to go across and give him an opinion on the arboretum at
Grimwood Grange that one of my ancestors had shown Capability
Brown how to plan.

"As I walked into the breakfast room and drew back the
curtains, I saw this owl sitting on one of the lamp holders of our
American organ that once belonged to Bach.

"Obviously, too, it was an intelligent owl, for I had been
playing a fugue the night before, and in addition to pages of
music having been turned, Grandmother's glasses were folded
back quite neatly on the other lampholder. Owls can see in the
dark remember!"

The operator's brain was hot on the capping trail. I knew the
signs. He was nodding all the time, and looking far away.

So I pressed on: "I looked at the owl for some while, and it
seemed to wink at me. However, time was pressing. I had to let

the owl out and there was not time enough to mesmerise the visitor — a technique I had perfected with eagles in the Caucasus. So I would just have to let him out.

"The door, though, was adjacent to the organ. However, I came to the view that this obviously intelligent, if unorthodox entrant, would prefer a dignified exit via the window.

"So I opened the window, which was fitted with a security bar because of the Rembrandts, and I beckoned and pointed in a suitable way to the musical owl."

"'You must be joking. You must improve on that! I am a sophisticated owl.' It was clear by its eyes that those were its thoughts.

"I paused for a moment. Then I got the gen. I went upstairs, reached my RAF tunic out of the wardrobe, gave the medal ribbons a quick polish, shoved the old 'scrambled egg' on my head and marched downstairs.

"This went down very well with the owl, which I noticed had carefully put the spectacles back in their case. It sat up to attention.

"Then I had to remember the exact marshalling procedure — Biggin Hill, eh! I encouraged a first sortie. But the owl, evidently not appreciating my effort, took off and flew around the room, wobbling dangerously near an aspidistra in Grandmother's favourite jardinier before landing again. It seemed to sigh as it settled down and looked at me. A look of pained nostalgia was apparent.

"A second circuit saw it bank towards the window, but it overshot and had to land again. The drill was coming back to me, though, and the next trip saw the owl do a victory roll — which I thought was very admirable and decent — before side-slipping through the window to the outside world.

"I quickly had my breakfast and rushed across to have a few jars with Sir Toby Smallbore."

"Firewater, you said!" said the suspended operator.

"Smallbore was there too," I replied. "And a hell of a day we had. But that's another story. When I returned in the evening, Gran was sitting in the chair.

"'I don't know what has been going on,' she said, 'but the

room was frightfully sooty according to the forward little madam who deigns to get my breakfast, mornings. The girl said there was this egg on the table over there, and that she nearly decided to use it for breakfast.'

"'It is an owl's egg,' I quickly chipped in."

Then looking straight at the nigh desperate 'operator', I continued: "Now you're just the bloke to tell me. What does an owl omelette taste like?"

A slurp, a splutter and the operator was gone.

The landlord smiled, and I was just going to chat to him when he said he could hear 'that damned phone again'.

Alec the roadman won't talk — not until he has had four pints. So I left.

When I went back the other day all the customers except Alec — who winked — rushed out, and the landlord said the vet had just arrived to see his wife — I mean, cat.

You can't win, can you!

Another pitch lost.

Passing the Tests

I WAS in a village tavern near Ottery St Mary.

The usual record — which is surely responsible for the peculiarities of so many landlords — was not on the turntable. There was no boasting of gardening progress, nor deceitful talk of a casual, behindhand attitude designed to divert attention from secret determined efforts at firstmanship with crops. All the talk was about Farmer Muddicombe's missus.

"Er've got past the post at last — after six outings," said Fred.

"Just as well," added Ted. "I yerd Farmer was going to tackle her tutor and examiner bloke. He told me when I was helping to rack his cider that he thought er must be having an affair with one or tother or both on em."

"Well, I reckon they did have to sit pretty tight up in thik little Mini," said Len. "Stands to reason. Look at the size of er!"

"Perhaps ee stood on the running board," suggested Mark.

"There baint no running boards now," returned Ted. "They'm out o' date — obnoxious, or whatever tis — like landlords who primed your cup in a proper manner."

The landlord did not react, but merely continued with his umpteenth attempt to manipulate sixteen names into a house darts competition.

At that point the voices faded away for me and I found myself in Grandfather's barn. I was about nine years old. It was November '38 or '39, and the weather was raw, cold, rainy, and windy.

"I want you to go up to the passun's fields," said Grandfather. "He wants the cider cheese to 'arbour the pheasants. You can drive while your uncle pitches the cheese up into the middle of the hedge." The cheese being the straw and squashed apple mixture left over from the cider-making process.

Anyway, we loaded the cart, and in the miserable rain we rumbled off to the glebe fields.

I wasn't very keen. There was the weather, the certainty of seeing no-one, the image I had of parsimonious parsons; and Uncle Arthur, I recall, wasn't in a very good mood.

Along the margin of the field we went, with me in charge of the shunts while Uncle flung the apple-straw residue up into the 'comb' of the hedge. Then a gateway loomed up. Narrow it seemed to me! I was ready to hand over the reins.

"You'm the carter," said a voice behind me. "Hold both reins firm and put the oss through the middle of the getway. The cart'll follow, I reckon."

In the rain and the wind I sat tense as our conveyance rumbled onwards: first ears in the middle of the gap, then shafts, and then an uncomfortable look sideways as the near post passed to the rear. Rattle! Rumble! went the broad wheels and I was half ready for a collision, which never came.

I had made it!

I had passed the test.

Then I was not sitting on a chair in the pub anymore, or on the corner of a cart, but in a 1935 Ford 8 just outside the Examiner's H Q at Barnstaple, sometime in '54.

My driving test was over, and the Examiner was sitting fiddling about with bits of paper.

I hadn't done badly, I thought, though I had managed to get jammed into traffic at one stage, and had leaned on the kerb on the turn.

The fiddling with paper carried on, and I was trying to look sideways, but my nose seems always to get in the way.

Would I make it?

Could I, who had in appalling conditions, with precise touch and utmost skill coaxed a fickle mare and a broad-wheeled cart betwixt Scylla and Charybdis, fail on a June day with a governable, predictable automobile? The idea grew agonising.

'I must pass!' I insisted to myself. 'You've got to let me through.'

'How could I possibly fail!' I rationalised.

After some moments the examiner enquired whether I had a car of my own and how far I would be driving, and after advising caution, etc., gave me the piece of paper I wanted.

'Of course I knew I had passed! It was inevitable,' I exulted within.

With *my* record how could I have possibly failed? Justice had been done.

Then I was back on the chair in the tavern again.

"Hey, schoolmaster," shouted someone. "Would ee like to get on television?"

"What's that!" I returned.

"Farmer Muddicombe's missus passed her test with such high marks ers having a go at the Monte Carlo rally," said Ted.

"Er wants a mate," added Fred.

"And you'm just the kiddie," went on Luke.

"The old man's afeared some fool's going to run away with her," said Mark.

"But he wouldn't mind a schoolmaster being co-pilot. You baint strong enough to carry her off, anyhow," ventured Ted.

"He's not in her class as a driver!" mocked Mark. "Look at the tuition and practice er've had."

"Did ee ever take any driving test, Schoolmaster?" added Fred.

"Let's have yer pedigree," demanded Ted.

"I had two tests," I said, "I passed both — first time."

"What did er say?" asked Luke.

"Ee's going maze," said Mark.

"The kids at Nuncombe have drove'n off is ead. Us shouldn't laugh," wagged Fred. "Us should feel sorry. Us might get like it ourselves one day."

The landlord flung a crumpled piece of paper on the pyramid in the ashtray and began to water his plastic flowers.

At that, I drank up, made the appropriate signal, accelerated to the bar entrance and manoeuvered precisely through.

Stookophobia

I WALKED into a tavern the other evening where I found a chap I have known from earliest schooldays taking the strain of the bar, as fairly usual.

I sensed he was preoccupied with something, and I very gently eased into a conversation, mentioning the weather, the abundance of apples, how many craneflies there were about, and that sort of thing.

Then I said, "What are you up to these days? How's the combining coming along?"

"We'm getting over it, I suppose," he said. "But we've got a dozen acres to cut with the binder." Here he laughed — in order not to weep, I fancy — and I knew then why he had been meditating.

My companion swilled his cider around in his cup, and whether or not there was a message in that, I felt under the circumstances I ought to buy him a drink.

"Boss always grows a field of wheat," my friend went on, "and we cut it and comb the straw for thatching reed."

"You can't pick it right up behind the binder?" I queried.

"No," came the reply, "it will all have to be stooked up." At this point my mate took out his handkerchief, turned away, and blew his nose.

I wanted to cheer him up, somehow — dig up a crumb of comfort if you like — and I said "I suppose there'll be a few around to do the stooking job!" but I found I wasn't on the right track at all.

For my friend misemployed a laugh again in a way that touched me, before he said, "I shall have to do the job. Well, I could possibly get a bit of help." And from that point I'm afraid, readers, I have to report another instance where I have not come up to scratch.

You see I have done a good many miles of stooking corn in the past, and I could have said, "Let me know when you're on the go, and I'll come across and give you a hand!" I could have — but I

didn't. I just could not push myself over the precipice, so to
speak, for as I helped to keep the bar of the Wyndham Arms in
position, I drifted off into a nostalgic and melancholy mood
myself as I pictured twelve acres of wheat standing there bold
and thick, and saw a binder flailing around, kicking out the
sheaves mechanically as if it could not care less. . .

I felt the rough corn stalks against my arms, and my weary
legs kicking one sheaf apart from its neighbour. I felt the sun,
and saw the long concentric traverse to the centre of the field,
where lay blessed release from bruised, stinging shins; and I
didn't have it in me to say, "I'll give ee a hand boy!" but in a
while had sloped off with a growing feeling of inadequacy.

Then the next step was of course to invent reasons why I
couldn't have helped: the distance of my mate's pad; the fact of
being out of practice; pressure of work — you know.

I wasn't very convinced, until I suddenly remembered:

"Give me a and to stick up some corn!" A farmer had said to
me. "I'll see you gets a drink."

Well, this was some twenty-odd years ago, when I was a hard-
up student; and I duly arrived in the harvest field around six
o'clock, and began to start stooking all on my own. There was
no cider jar, and during the evening the binder finished its
work, and was packed up and taken off to another field.

At that point I collared the boss and I said "I don't fancy this
solitary business. Is anyone coming down tomorrow?"

"Harry will be down," he said — Harry being an old boy who
worked when the pressure was on.

At that I cheered up and arrived pretty early next morning in
that twelve acre field, confident that Harry would soon appear.
He didn't. By dinner time he hadn't arrived, nor by tea, and as it
grew dark I knocked off feeling right sulky; no drink, no mate.
The following morning the same thing happened, and I wearily
wound around towards the centre of the field. Suddenly I
realised the end was in sight, and I had an idea which caused me
to brighten up and put on a spurt. I thought to myself 'I shall
finish about eleven thirty, and then I'll cycle off to the The Four
Horse Shoes and charge the "Harry will be down, see you gets a
drink," operator until dinnertime. It will serve him right!'

Can you guess what happened? As I picked up the very last sheaf a large red-faced farmer came in the gate of the field. I could have... Let's say I was mad!

So perhaps you will try to understand why I couldn't bring myself to offer a hand to my mate. You will surely agree that I had this altogether unpleasant experience in a twelve acre field. In any case I am too busy.

Oh dear, there I go rationalising again. Perhaps I should offer to bathe my friend's shins — or buy him another pint. But that doesn't seem...

I think I had better close the subject.

Price of Scrumpy

THE CLOCK'S tick supplied the background music in The Corn Drill. Harry and Sid, who were sitting next to each other could have been taken for garden gnomes, while Frank the cowman had his head stuck in the evening paper. Jack the landlord seemed to be trying to polish a sleever and turn it inside-out in the one operation.

Suddenly Frank cleared his throat, and Harry with a concentrated effort turned ever so slightly to wink at Sid, who was shuffling beer mats around the table.

"According to this yer, yer, zider is going up to seventy dree pence a pint, which is, een my reckning, nearly fifteen bob in old money," informed Frank.

"Zure to be right!" nodded Harry. "Marvellous clever."

"Ow d'ee mean?" asked Frank.

"You be — marvellous clever — working out thik sum," said Harry.

"Considering ee adds up instead of taking away on the dart board!" observed Sid.

"Zay you walks in yer, vergets yersel Arry, and calls ver a pint for you and Zid. Then you'd be thirty bob wuss off," persisted Frank.

"And I'd be zummin else," said Harry, "I'd be gone maze."

"*You'm* talking!" said Frank. "But we'm in the Market and they've got their rules and thats the be-all and aand-all of it."

"*You'm* in the Market — if you like," said Sid, "but I didn join. I voted 'no' and zo did Arry."

"That I didn't" retorted Harry. "I put — "

"We know what you put on the ballot paper!" chipped in the landlord.

"Iggerant!" remarked Frank the cowman.

"Owsomever, whatever message you zaand em, we'm in the Community and scrumpy is gwain to be classed as wine."

"Wull," said Harry, "cum to think of it, tis purt near as dear as wine now: thirty pence a pint, which according to me reckoning is six bob a pint."

"I can remember when was drippence — in old money," said Sid, "and they old clome cups wuz good measure too!"

"I think," said Jack the Landlord, polishing and twisting faster than usual, "that the cider sold over the bar will not be haffected by any noo rules of the EEC."

"Ow?" jerked Sid belligerently.

"Because," went on the landlord, "the new rules that they are talking about refer to farmhouse cider."

"Whass the difference between varm ouse zider and what comes out of thik polythene job you got there?" asked Frank.

"A ell of a lot!" said Sid.

"Very little nowadays," replied the landlord. "The zider makers have gone into it scientifically and come up with a very fine product."

"Ee's right!" said Harry, and the landlord nodded, gratefully.

"Ee's right!" repeated Harry, and the landlord made room on his cheeks for a practised smirk.

"Old Farmer Spout ed it taped," continued Harry, "the scientific job I mean. 'Pub zider, be watered science' he zed. 'Vull o' chemicals'."

The landlord instantly countermanded instructions to his face, and fiddled about with an optic.

"Everybuddy naws" said Frank the cowman, "that zider be vighting juice — rots your socks —"

"Varm zider" interrupted Harry, "will zort out the maen vrum the boys right nuff. But this yer stuff evn't got nowhere near the same poke."

"I sell enough of it!" returned the landlord.

"Ees," said Sid, "that you do. But us evn't got no choice ev us!"

"*Some* landlords round about here don't sell cider!" informed the landlord.

"And they wants pole axing!" cut in Harry. "When in Devon, you do like the Romans. The point is varm zider be real zider and makes ee cheerful and like you've ed a drink, while tother stuff makes ee feel miserable — like you've bin robbed."

"Wull, I baint coming in yer when you fellers ev to fork out fifteen bob ver a pint," resumed Frank the cowman. "Twon't be safe."

"I've told you all," said Jack the landlord deliberately, "that it isn't going to happen in pubs. According to the trade paper — the cider that goes over the counter —"

"Iddn't strong enough to be taxed," chipped Harry, "and proper varm zider that ev got a bit of go in it, ev zeemingly got to go dru the mill."

"The ole world be upsidown if you asks me," offered Sid.

"Must be," said Jack the landlord, "because those French blokes you were tutoring on table skittles last night, left a couple of pints in over for you two chaps. Of course, feeling like you do about the pub cider and the Market —"

Here there was a pause. In The Corn Drill Frank the cowman smirkingly shoved his nose in the paper, while Harry and Sid ever so quietly drank up, and placing their cups on the counter, changed back into garden gnomes — and waited.

Still Eggers — een the Debn dialect

ZUM FELLER was tullin me tuther day that ee yerd ees vather zay that zum vokes used to take the dregs — us calls em drugs — of zider, and make still eggers (distilled liquor).

"They got zum feller to make a still," ee zed, "and atter they'd finished wae un they ide'n away zum place."

Well of course twuz genst the law, and every wips wile zomebody got collared ver it.

I bide listening to the yarn and thinking like us do in Debn, ow I was going to cap ees tale; and thik chap must ev zid I was getting vacant, ver me mind was turning awver a tale Granfer told me dunkeys years ago. Any road I jumped een: "My Granfer was Charlie Goff," I zed, "and ee farmed Guddiford Mills, which is lower side of Kaansbeare, and what you'm saying calls to mind a story ee told of what appened at the turn of the zaanchury."

Granfer ed vower or vive brothers, and they wanted to ev a go at making still eggers. But their vather was bout as ard as nails and they dursn make a move as they wuz afeared the old feller would vind out and play up merry ell.

Well they bided their time, and in due course a chance cum along when the old man caught the 'monia. Purty bad ee ad it — wudn expected to come round — so Granfer and the rest aw'm thought twould be a good time to ev a go at making zum still eggers.

When you comes to think awt they must ev bin a pretty vine paasul of ellers.

Owsomever they coyducted the local blacksmith down to Guddiford Mills, and atter they'd lashed un up wae zider ee agreed to knock up zum sort of still.

"Like a gurt grammerphone orn," Granfer zed, "Us chucked a voo bucketfuls of drug zider een the copper, put the still on the top and then clayed round the join. Then us lighted a vire, and vor long zummin or other dripped out ot the spout ot the contraption and een to the bucket."

It zims that this caper went on ver the best part of a wik, avore things beginned to go wrong, ver the ole man started to pule round and buck up no aend, and everybody started erning round like blue arsed flies.

Bottles of still eggers wuz poked eento the corn beens at the top of the mill, and when the gaffer started straaking about again everything zimmed regler and sueant.

Mind you, Granfer zed that the smell of the job aanged round ver ell of a time. Een vact they thought twould stick about till kingdom come.

Even the village bobby — that's yer Community Police long avore twuz thought ov — remarked on the curious smell, when ee called een ver ees daily ration of zider.

The Next Object is Vegetable

I WONDER if you recall the rhyme 'Three Jovial Huntsmen', who apparently went hunting, and 'nothing could they find except'... well, now there's the rub: what did they find?

Apparently a hare was turned up:

> The first said it was a hare
> The second said, Nay;
> The third said it was a calf,
> And the cow had run away.

From the above you will get a pretty good idea of the intellectual calibre and/or eyesight of two of the gentlemen.

Don't worry though, such capers do not occur these days. Surely not? Correct! But you can get somewhat similar situations.

For instance, there was an astute farmer who struggled into The Corn Drill in the fall of the year, when no one but the host and myself was around.

He plonked down a certain vegetable, and hurriedly gasping out the prodigious statistics of the 'swede', hopped it before any of the blokes who had helped him on the bale cart came in. No comment!

Such a fellow, who had been excitedly watching points from over a wall and had belted up on his bike, entered the bar, cursing his wasted effort.

"Eh, what the ell's that!" he jerked out, on regaining breath.

"A swede," replied the landlord, who added for good measure that in Blankshire they carried out swede wine to the haymakers, to drive them, one projects, to work their way into the *Guinness Book of Records* — or on to oblivion.

No surprise at the dimensions of the swede was shown by Farmer Spout, alias Munchhausen, who came in closely followed by Sid, Harry, and George. The yeoman, given to exaggeration, maintained that various acquaintances all distant, deceased — or both — would if present, vouch for larger swedes than the crimson exhibit that by then seemed to be making up to a red polycask.

"Is it oller?" queried Sid, and he whipped round the corner of the bar when the landlord went off to fetch a log.

"Ee baint!" was the verdict.

"Ow eavy do ee reckon then?" asked Harry.

"More'n a score," offered George, who 'wudn evin any truck with that thur metrification.'

By then Jack the landlord was in the offing and the swede was hurriedly reinstated. There was a pause.

"My carrots ed the fly, this year," eased Sid, mischieviously.

"Thass nothing extraudnry ver a carrot!" countered Farmer Spout, swinging round to defend, as of habit, out of necessity. "Without a word of a lie —"

"I do zim to recall trenching round turnips awver by Little Stitchbury," chipped Harry, winking none too artfully.

Munchhausen capped and frustrated, stubbed out his fag and left, just as Tom entered.

At that the conversation suddenly lurched from the best wood for stems of beetles employed in the wedging apart of purple cabbages, onto gardening.

"That swede is probably blown up with artificial or made of polythene," sneered Tom, a keen gardener who was still rattled at being 'fiddled out of best parsnip' in the Flower Show.

I went out thereabouts, and I swear that the mangold which seemed to me to be growing remarkably like mine host, nodded ever so slightly — and smiled.

Eddication versus Dialect

I WAS eving a drink tuther day in a village pub when zum feller vrum awver genst Sheldon zed to me: "How do you manage schoolmaster? I mean, you talk real Devon. With all your education, and bearing in mind you're teaching youngsters — how is it the people who trained you didn't knock all the dialect out of you?"

I swilled me zider round in me mug a couple of times, and thought yer a bit avore I answered. But zeeing as I wudn gwain to get any place I thought I may as well eddicate the feller a bit — and drink up and go up to the manger sarta opefully, atter I'd gone all round the bushes — like I purt near always do. So I zed "Aw yes Archie Painter, the village skulemaaster, tried all ee nawd to knock zum of the dialect out of me — and the rest aw us. He didn't make much aadway I'll tull ee. Owsummever I did vind mesel one Saturday morning, in the back of Beel Western's butcher's van on the road to Cullompton to zit ver the scholarship — as they called it.

"Zummow or nuther I passes — twas in '40 — and in doo course I vound mesel een Tiverton Boys' Middle Skule. In ther words I was a mudscraper, and twadn very long avore Tom Jenkins the English Maaster wuz evin a go at zum aw us on account of our spaich.

"Ee — Jenks us called'n — used to cum een the classroom, take out his gold timepiece and zay: 'I'm waiting! We've lost faive minutes already', which was purty anzum I thought as the lying old toad edn ardly cum dru the door. Jenks wadna bad feller really, but like I zed ee couldn't leave the language alone. Not ee!

"I can mind that twadn no time at all avore ee was stuffing Keats' 'Ode to Autumn' down our drauts, and when zum boy read 'Or by a zider press with patient look', Jenks went purt near off ees aad.

" 'Cidah!' thik skulemaster ollered, 'It's cidah — not zider — you fathead.'

" 'Tis zider wae us you'll vind, you maze aaded vurriner,' I thought, ver Jenks cum from Bangor. 'When in Debn you do like the Romans!' I thought that as well!"

At this point I swilled me zider around and ed a swig. But the uther feller didn't catch on — zo I wuz forced to take up me tale again.

So I zed "Mind you us didn mind playing Jenks up vairish, as eed cough and splutter and then take out ees watch all awver agen — which wuz more entertaining than *King Lear* or *Lorna Doone.*

"And zum ov tuther teachers at Tiverton used to ev a go at zum ov us ver our manner ov spaaking, but I don't think they made much cloth ov us; and as us wadn daft enough to put ennything down in writing a gude voo ov us got what Mother called Skule Cerstifiket.

"'School Certificate before Marriage Certificate', the aadmaster, Joe Duffin used to zay when ee zeed a boy anging a zatchel belonging to one of Miss 'eyworth's girls on a lamp post. That wuz ow you shawed yer affection in they days; and I should tull ee that Miss 'eyworth — Miss H the maidens called er — was aadmistress of Tiverton Girls' Middle Skule.

"We wuz separate in the same building — if you gets me maaning — and I can tull ee that the classroom genst the ockey pitch wuz much sought atter, ver every wips while a girl would go top-an-tail. And I'm able to tull ee was well, that they girls wore reglation navy blue knickers, and twuz a wonder there wudn more trouble than there wuz, as thee cusen get cateepult lastic ver love nor money. There wuz a war on, zee."

Round about yer, I stopped and ed another pull at me pint, but tuther feller seemed very eenterested een the tale I was telling — staring like a pole cat ee was — so I thought I'd best carry on.

"Wur wuz I? Aw yes, I went from TBMS into various jobs avore I wuz conscripted into the RAF. Then zummin must ev come awver me one day when I wuz drinking a pint of Coate's zider in the NAAFI at RAF Yatesbury, ver I zed to mesel: 'Anged if I don'e ev a go at skulemaistering!' Silly fule!

"Anny road I paaned a letter and atter filling in a voo vorms I

ed to go up in vrunt of Jimmy Smeall, the principal or aad man
at St Luke's College.

"Ee asked me a passul of questions about mesel, eddication,
and a voo more about Rugby, and then ee shoved a book in me
aand and told me to read one of they thur poems by a feller by the
name of Byron.

"I was reading dru avoraand like, trying to get everything
suent when I noticed a word thur: W-R-A-C-K.

"Ah, I thought, me ole cock sparrer you've got in een yer aad
that I'm going to zay thik word wrong. Perhaps maister, you
thinks I'm mump aaded — put een wae the braad and tooked out
wae the cakes, zart o' thing.

"I wuz smiling to mesel as I beginned to read, till the principal
feller ollered out: 'Louder!'

"I read the piece again, but Jimmy must ev got out on the
wrong zide of the baad ver ee keeped on bout reading louder.

"I remember thinking to mesel 'This yer louder caper is
draiving me genst the aadge. I shall chuck the book at ee and tull
ee to read the poem yerself, avore long, maister'.

"I reckon Maister Smeall zid I was getting ratty as ee' old ees
osses ver a bit! Then atter saying zummin about a shortage of
Rural Studies teachers, ee zed zummin else about provisional
acceptance — whatever that maaned. As a matter ov vact I
wondered if I might not aand up like Betty Muxworthy vaading
the pigs ver Jan Ridd.

"But I didn, and St Luke's and taaching ver dunkeys' years ev
taanded to att zum ov the dialect outa me aad."

Round about yer, the feller I was tulling to slipped out of ees
chair. I can't tell ee ver why. I elped un back, ed a sip of zider,
waited aaf a minute, swilled me mug around, and zeeing twadn
no good, I went on spouting.

"I find," I said, "that one grows haway from the mode of speech
hemployed in one's childhood and youth; and I vinds I slips back
mostly in taverns when there's a voo vizitors about — and me
cup's purt near empty." I zed that last bit two or dree times avore
I was forced to carry on wae me tale.

"Jest imagine zum youngster is disrupting the class! Well

thee cusen very well zay: 'If thee disn prick een a stick young feller-me-lad, I'll githee a vairish ole zonnicker, you ockerd little eller!' No zur! "And mores the pity!" I zed.

Atter a bit I keened around and zid the feller I'd bin eddicating ed gone, and when I axed the landlord ee zed eed cleared off a vair bit ago, higgerant eller — atter I'd bin a trying to giv'n a simple answer to ees question.

Owsomever jest as the landlord zed that thik flibbertigibbit of a barmaid vace painted all colours and eyes like they pandas thhez zee at the zoo, come flouncing een all la-di-da like. Old Abe come in too, and a young traveller feller. I made strawks out the back and I couldn't elp but notice thik maid sort of tittered, and flinged ersel about cuz I knew erd want to make a fuss of the youngster, leaving me to put up wae Abe's old wickpot.

Any road, when I cum back er was looking as stickle as a rook. Er banged down Abe's pot and purt near chucked ees change at un, avore ee zarted out ees money, arged bout the weather, the price of new teddies, the 14-18 — and purt near everything else.

Well thik barmaid kept on sticking out er jib and giving me black looks. I tull ee er near nuff ed a blue fit when I told thik rep bloke the tale, and coyducted un onto the bandit. And when ee att the jackpot, and stood, Passchendaele — Abe I maan — and me, both aw us a pint, er eyes went round like two turmits in a wheelbarra.

Well, thik zilly young feller recharged er glass as well, to tell ee the rights of it, and er cracked er chops vairish and you could have mistook er ver a lovesick caav. And thik green orn valled right een and ee axed Big Bertha — that's what us calls er — when er knocked off work.

Zo it all ended up pretty well in the aand. Although dialect is eenclined to get ee labelled as a clodhopper, and take ee round the bushes, it gan get ee places where thees want ver tu get, in the aand.

I got me drink, and zo did Abe. Thik wench behind the bar, er did all right — though a couple of snorts to er is like sarring a donkey wae a strawberry.

I can't tell ee if er clicked with thik johnny fortnight, but I reckon ee broke fence, fer I ebn zid un zince. And when I axed er

— and I wadn sniggerin or nuthin — bout the feller, er zed zummin about ee was, er expected, minding ees own business — and I reckon er naws zummin bout me getting landed wae Exeter City in the sweep.

Leaving aside er behind the bar, eddication is a very good thing I naw, but the Debn spaach can bring home the bacon ver they what naws the ropes.

Perhaps though you may be gwain to zay zummin bout the feller I was telling to, ee that valled off ees chair, and then slawped off — dungeel eller.

Well disn thee worry bout ee! Like I zed ee cums from tuther side ov Sheldon, and ees great grandfather cum yer een zum depression or nuther. Cum the spring of the year, ee — thik bloke vrum Sheldon — wears a daffodil een ees forelock, and an onion in ees weskit pocket. Zo ees a vurriner and us ebn got to worry nort 'tall bout un. Like I zed.

I'll zay cheerio naw. Keep skatting vore. And mind the morning.

Debn ver Ever!

THAT BRAZEN feller they interviewed on the wireless a bit back, who seemed intent on forming a Cockney-Cornish Association came as no surprise to me. No Sir! You could say that in one way or another as a Devon Nationalist I have been ploughing a lonely furrow to keep back the tide that only a very small minority of natives seem to have sniffed. And if that isn't a perfect example of mixed metaphors, what is?

Who would expect that in Cornwall where it appears there is a fierce pride in Mebyon Kernow, some stannary caper and a special language, an ethnic minority from the smoke would dare to push its luck, advancing fortified with pease pudding, and lobbing faggots. The Cornish — Cousin Jacks to us Devonions — are to be shoved off the pavement, requiring to touch the forelock to ignorant rag-tags from Tottenham, who have seemingly never heard of Exeter City or Torquay Athletic — or even Plymouth Argyle.

The very idea! Cornishmen are of course vurriners to all of us who were born and bred in Devon — that jewel set in a silver sea — as Will Shakespeare — who in fact was none other than Walt Raleigh — has aptly put it. But like I said, this Cockney take-over bid is the sort of job I have been harping about for 'ell of a time now.

It is to be hoped that blatant and cocky enterprise in Cornwall will make everybody worth anything in Devon put down their cider mugs — if they can get any scrumpy — and do a bit of thinking. If they are like me they will realise that the fate threatening the Duchy has practically overcome Devon already.

Let me illustrate. If and when you've got a minute or two I'd like to invite you to chat up the boss bureaucrats on the County Council and then switch across to the Districts. Collar a feller and ask'n if ees veeling purty viddy, ask'n what is meant by 'nort', 'thiky thur' and 'coming back leery'. Rub your palm across yer firkin and shove'n across to a chief officer, and see if he flinches. You'll soon uncover a passel of refugees.

Take eddification for instance!

You've got one of they taffs from Anglesey in charge there, and he took over from a fellow barbarian. In fact tis more like a dynasty than an eddication outfit in County Hall. Haven't us got nobody born and bred in God's own county sufficiently well eddicated to run the show? I tell ee straight I'd have had a bash years ago in my younger days, and then you'd have more of the three r's, more stick, less jargon — and to ell with working parties. Yes Sir!

And look at Dartmoor. Wouldn't you think that you'd find a local in charge there! Not on your life. We've got a feller from Yorkshire — running our moor. Well tis our own fault. Who gidn the job? Do you think for a minute there's a likely lad from Moretonhampstead overseeing the Yorkshire Wolds? I'll bet there idn.

Which reminds me. Hands up all those who want another ration of Rugby League when the rugby season begins again! For donkeys years us ev ed to listen to Eddie Waring & Co hollering and shouting the odds about games in the North of England that us couldn't care less about.

Having been a conscript in the RAF I don't want to be reminded about Warrington — and Padgate. And tell me this: do you reckon the people in Lancashire are being served up Tiverton versus Newton Abbot, on a Saturday afternoon? Perhaps us could club together in Devon and organise a charabanc for the hatful of Rugby League blokes about the place.

Walk into a pub like I did the other day — a country local, on the River Tale about three miles from Ottery — and order a pint of draught cider. What do ee find? Some vurriner behind the bar looks down his nose at yours truly like he was something the cat dragged in and says all superior like, in an alien twang: "I don't do the draught any more! It encourages undesirables."

I had half a mind to yank ees simulated beard and tell'n that when you'm in Devon you does like the Romans, until I realised he was a rusty gurt toad, a good bit younger than mesel. Surely this notion of importing erbs who chuck out the native brew shows how the county of Devon has been infiltrated and largely taken over during the recent past.

Do you imagine for a moment that Frank Drake, Jack Hawkins and old Walt over at Hayes Barton wouldn't have had any truck wae it? They'd have played up merry ell, I'll tull ee!

So I'm gwain to ask all the remaining genuine natives of Devon to come under my Devon Nationalist banner and take steps to repel the hinsidious hinvasion of our homeland. I reckon us needs a radio station broadcasting in Devon dialect and a new coat of arms based on a firkin — ver a start.

I'll arrange a meeting somewhere behind Blackborough. Bring a jar of scrumpy, a pickled onion or two, bread and cheese, a pasty — and clean dung forks.

Us'll form a constitution, have a game of skittles, guggle back the refreshment — and I should be able to put over my policies in a language pure-bred natives will understand.

Ang on a minute! Perhaps you'd better bring two jars of scrump.

Wyless Years Agone

MY EMMERS ow time flies! Us don't realise it till summin crops up and us sees it in the paper or yers it on the radio.

Now, us ev just bin reminded that thur bin wyless een Debn ver sixty yers — and that makes ee think, don't it!

I minds that us ed a wyless avore twuz time ver me to go to Kaansbeare skule, in '34. Een a master gurt box thik wyless wuz, and my brother and I used to think there must be some vuller een behind like, who'd tull es every now'n agen that us wuz listening to the National Programme vrum London.

I always minds that, cuz my younger brother Dennis — who wuz forever thinkin bout ees belly — used to zay the feller een behind was tulling about the National Pudden vrum London.

Theez naw, not very many vokes nawed ort tall bout wylesses in they days. Arry Zellick over Wood Lane, an eddicated and terrible long-aaded feller who weared plus fours, ee did. Ee made a set, and I've zid un bide listening to un ver ages, as if zummin wadn quite the ticket. Eed plug zarten instreements eento the wyless, and listen. Eed twist knobs and thik wyless of ees would oller and scraim blue murder.

But I'm gwain away vrum me tale. Vather was an eller for poking our wyless bout wae a screwdriver, and I reckon ee done it wance too often, ver atter one go there wadn no more 'national pudden', and us children wuz told us would ev to wait until Vather won a snowball whist or Mother cum up on the Devon draws vor us ed another set.

Owsomever us didn ev to wait that long as it appened, ver zum johnnie fortnight feller came in one night wae a smart looking job. I mind twas a 'Monarch', and ee wanted vive guineas ver'n.

Mother bide scratching er aad ver zum time and then er made a deal — zo much down and zo much a wik. "Lord a mercy! Ow shall pay, evven alone naws!" er zed, and though I musn take the good Lord in vain, now, I know that as a child I thought er zart o' prayer was answered, ver tiz zartin zure us never zid air ner ide ov the feller again.

Thik set wuz a booty I thought. But Vather reckoned ee wadn quite the ticket, and off come the back and thur wuz the innards, out on the kitchen table. Vather smawked ees pipe and zimmed to naw what he was doing and I naw I wuz very eenterested as pieces of teen on a zart o'speendle went vore and back. But thik wyless zimmed to ev a mind of ees own, ver ee chucked een one night when Vather was 'adjusting un' and Mother would ev played up merry ell I'm zure, only thik very zame day Longie vrum Uffculme, the paper feller, falled awver aad and busted our wet battery eed charged up.

Zee the snag wuz us didn't understand enough about the wyless caper in they days and wull-maaning vokes could do more arm than good. Mind you, my Vather's cousin must ev éd a knack ver wylesses, ver ee come up one Zaturday arnoon, atter eed bin over The Vore Oss Shoes, and as usual he wuz ready to arge the toss about everything under the zin. Ee zart o skammelled een dru the kitchen and made ver to zit on the table. The table tipped up and our Ekco wyless slide off — wet battery, high tension, grid battery and all — on to the vloor.

Caw, didn Mother carry on! Er rattled on to zich an extaant that Vather's cousin gid up any cantakus notions, and kneeled down and got the wyless back together again. And do you naw, thik wyless went better atter thik little outin, and Mother zed zummin about "shaking ees liver up!"

But Georgie Beer, ee that stood to work up Bishops Farm, wadn nort like as nawing as Vather and ees cousin, and one day ee let out ow higgerant ee really wuz.

Thur wuz a gang of vullers out oeing — twuz during the '39 war. George was spoutin bout 'radiolocation'.

"Thik radiolocation caper finds the jerry planes, and downs um!" zed George, as ee vooled up ees pipe.

"Don't thee be su maze!" zed Varmer Tom, the gaffer.

"Whaddy maan?" George went on stivverin up.

"What I maans," zed Farmer Tom, "is you'm talking dru yer at; ver the radiolocation vinds the planes, right enough, but our fellers goes up and shets em down."

"Don't thee talk zich a lot ov wickpot, Guvnor!" George vired back, and things got zo vimmit that Farmer Tom banged down ees oe and went een varm to vetch the paper and "draive zummin into thee gurt mump aad, George."

I naws this is right, cuz Mother zid Farmer Tom skammelling down past our ouse, vraming away to eesel alarmin.

While ees boss was provin un wrong, George went across and zawt down under a nut bush and bide there pulling et ees virkin; en ver wiks atterwards ee went round sniggering like, and zimmed to think ee'd bin mortal clever, zilly gurt toad.

Where wuz I? Aw yes. Sixty years of wyless zims to have vlied by — and us ev got better eddicated I spose. And things be aasier — more sosfixiated, like.

As long as a feller naws the difference between 'on' and 'off' and which vinger to push buttons wae, then ees laughin.

Just like thik George!

Passing the Tests   see page 15

Apple-Een-En Out

TWADN VERY appy awver tu Mudhayes, I'll tull ee. "Bessie," zed the missus, "I've bin maaning tu ev a word wae ee ver zum time. Theez bin moping bout ver wiks now, Maid. Whatever ails ee?"

"Well Missus," zed Bessie, "tis zummin to do wae Mother — ver a start anyway."

"Then spaak out Girl, and us'll chow it awver," zed Missus, "and zee if us can zart zummin out. Tis a pain tu zee ee!"

"Mother vails", zed Bessie, "er's gwain back a buster."

"Ow d'ee maan?" asked Missus.

"Well," zed the maid, "er ebn got no go een er t'all these days. Er got tu use both aands to drae round the mangle, and er don't zim take no eenterest een ersel. Er zits een the chimey corner raadin they love books, and every wips while er zarta snuffles like an old yaw, en wipes er vace een er old barass apern."

"Well, Maid," zed Missus, "the age is there. Us musn't verget ers zeventy-vower cum Michaelmas. Tis a vair age."

"Ees, I naws ers getting upalong, Missus," zed Bessie, "but up to a month ago er wuz lively as a cricket — and I blames thik ole varmer awver tu Claybeare —"

"Whatever d'ee maan, Maid?" zed Missus.

"Well, ever zince Vather passed away, ee bin cummin awver, wae a bag o' swedes, a brace of rabbits — zummin or nuther.

" 'Don't go cummin een like a good cheel if you zees the jardinier upsidown in the weenda,' Mother used to zay.

Now ee ebn bin een ver godnaws ow long, thik varmer, and tuther night atter er bin at the paasnip wine, Mother chucked thik jardinier at the grandfather clock. And now us don't naw where tis Christmas or Aaster."

"I spec er'll cum round in time, Maid," zed Missus. "Th' old 'oman zounds like a lovesick caav tu me."

"That's as maybe Missus," zed Bessie, "but the good Lord 'll take er one day ver zure — and there's me left — one be mesel.

"I've never ed a young man, to spaak ov Missus, and I gets tu thinking bout zich things lately — when you vinds me moping, that is."

"Now Maid," zed Missus, "I takes yer maaning zure nuff. I bin thinking you wuz getting zarta broody, and I bin scheming ver to elp ee."

"Ev ee now Missus!" nodded Bessie.

"Ees, I ave," said Missus, "and I reckons I've cum up wae an answer. *You* can draive the maister tu market, every Waansday, instead o' me."

"Me draive?" enquired Bessie, stivverin up.

"Zackly!" zed Missus. "Get theesel up a bit thereafter. Chuck away thik old bonnet, ev yer 'air done and pull yersel een round the middle. Get on o' they there brazers, they keeps on bout on the telly — and get a voo other bits and pieces that the maan-volk zims to like."

"Do ee really think I might click Missus?" zed Bessie.

"That I do!" zed Missus. "If you play yer cards right, thee'll coyduct zum feller zure nuff, and twill all be a change ver me. Ver Varty yers I've took thik drunken old eller to market where be vancies ees chances wae thik vast little ussy een the Dewdrop Een. Then ee valls across the zaat on the trap on the way awm, and when ee idn snoring, ees zinging 'Cum landlord vill the flowing bowl' or 'Awver the fields and turmits' — all on the one tune."

"Thanks Missus!" zed Bessie. "Us'll zee ow it goes."

Well dree or vore months went by and the Missus wuz getting zarta curious to naw ow things wuz gwain. So one day er catched up wae Bessie, when er was vaading the paags.

"Zit theesel down on this yer rail ver a minute or too, Maid," zed Missus. "I wants ver ee tu tull me ow things be gwain."

"Mother ev bucked up no aand," zed Bessie. "Thik old varmer ev cum snaaking back — on market afternoons. Mother ebn zed nort mind, but I vound a snuff teen on the dresser tuther day — and tis a wonder us don't look like rabbits."

"I'm very plaized," zed Missus, "But be een voo of a feller yet?"

"Oh Missus," zed Bessie, "I'm zo glad you asked me, ver I wuz getting on like a ouse on vire wae a paag varmer awver tu Slew

Pool, but now it ev zarta cooled down, zo to spaak."

"Gwan wae yer tale," zed Missus.

"Well," zed Bessie, "while Maister wuz een anging up at — I maan while Maister was doing business een the Dewdrop, thik feller, ev took to takin me een the Oss and Wheelbarra, ver a pasty and aaf a zider. Mindy ou I reckon eev done a main bit of oss daaling, ver ee keeped on patting me backside and veeling me legs where I wears me garters."

"Get on wae yer tale," zed Missus, "us ebn got all day, Maid."

"Well," zed Bessie, "ee — thik varmer, Beel ees called, asked me if I could draive a tractor, en ump bales around. Ee wanted to naw eef I could elp out wae the paperwork. I'd be an assistant ver a start, ee zed."

"I awp you zed you could do all ee wanted," zed Missus.

"Ees I did," zed Bessie, "Everything was gwain vamous, tull thik varmer asked me a zarten thing. And that zim to ev upset the apple cart."

"Lord or messy!" said Missus, "Whathever be on about?"

"Well," zed Bessie, "thik feller, thik feller — "

"Gwan," zed Missus, "thu feller —"

"Thik feller asked me if I could plain cook —"

"My ays I'm mortal plaized," zed Missus. "I was putting the cart avore the oss."

"Ees I can cook," I zed, and thik Beel zimmed appy, till ee zed 'Canst make dumplings, doughboys, brawn-and fry chitterling', and thurs zummin else."

"Gwan!" chipped een Missus. "Gwan!"

" 'Would ee, would ee—' " beginned Bessie.

"Gwan!" zed Missus. "Gwan! Us ebn got all day, Maid."

" 'Canst make apple-een-an-out ov a Zinday'," thik feller zed," zed Bessie.

"Lord a messy!" zed Missus, twisting er apern een knots. "I wondered what the devil thik feller was on upon."

" 'Whass apple-een-an-out?' I zed," went on Bessie, "and I could see thik fellers nose was outa joint, ver ee went turble quiet, and ee aat ees pasty and mine too; and ever zince eev zawt down een a corner ov the bar takin snuff, and eyeing me up and down from under ees Jim Crow at. Now I'm bested!"

"Disn thee worry maid," zed Missus, "ee'll cum back to the manger sure nuff."

"Oh Missus, do ee really think so?" zed Bessie.

"That I do!" zed Missus. "Vust of all I'll taach ee ow to make apple-een-an-out, and I'll come een wae ee ov a Waansday en giv thik Beel yer vool pedigree — en a piece of apple-een-en-out to go wae ees pasty —"

"Wull ee really Missus?" zed Bessie, "You do tak zich an eenterest in me."

"Ees, I do!" zed Missus, "But I wants ver ee tu understand two things, young lady. Us mustn't rush the job ver a start. And eef thees ever cum awm from market avore time, keen around, and look ver a jardinier, a upsidown jardinier, in the dairy weenda."

One Upmanship   see page 2

ACROSS COBBLE STONES by **D. V. Rugg.** East Devon Memoirs (Kentisbeare).

'Derrick Rugg recalls the sights, smells and characters familiar to his Devon Village.' *Times Educational Supplement*

'Idyllic childhood with a sombre end.' Peterborough, *Daily Telegraph*

'Short but vivid, full of affection, yet interest not nostalgia is aroused.' *Church Times*

'It should be on sale in every village shop.' *South West Review*

'Another regional gem from a publisher with a fine record in this field.' Judy Diss, *Herald Express*. Illustrated. 72pp. £2.60

A BOOK ABOUT SMUGGLING IN THE WEST COUNTRY, 1700 — 1850
by **Antony Hippisley-Coxe.** The author writes with an eye for those details that make history come alive.
The Times choice of interesting books.
'The best work of our time on the subject.' *Western Morning News*
Illustrated. 112pp. £6.95 hardback, £1.99 paperback.

THEM DAYS, from the memories of Joan Bellan by Joy Lakeman.
South West Devon (Buckland Monachorum)
'The voice of recent history.' *Western Morning News*
Illustrated. 128pp. £2.95

A YEAR AT POLVERRAS by Sylvia Ouston.
A novel drawing on the author's knowledge of Cornish rural life, set in the 1920s.
'Captivated me totally.' Susan Hill, *Good Housekeeping*
'Deserves the widest audience.' *Sunday Telegraph*
168pp. £6.95 hardback, £3.25 paperback

THE STORY OF A CORNISHMAN in Two Parts by Edward Prynn.
1: **A BOY IN HOBNAILED BOOTS**
   'The great fascination of this racy story ... it is nothing short of amazing.' *Western Morning News*
2: **NO PROBLEM**
   'Un-put-downable.' *Cornish Times*
   140pp. Both Illustrated, and at £2.95

POLLACK AND CARNIVAL: Cornish Short Stories by **Walter Walkham.**
'In this book Mr Walkham shows his flair for characterisation and a good yarn.' *Sunday Independent*. Illustrated. 64pp. £1.30